To develop
your child's gifts
and talents

ALMANAC

A Reference Workbook for Ages 6-8

Written by Mary Hill and Martha Cheney
Illustrated by Larry Nolte

Lowell House
Juvenile
Los Angeles

CONTEMPORARY BOOKS
Chicago

Manufactured in the United States of America

ISBN: 1-56565-236-3

10 9 8 7 6 5 4 3 2 1

Lowell House books can be purchased at special discounts when ordered in bulk for premiums and special sales.
Contact Department VH at the following address:
Lowell House Juvenile
2029 Century Park East
Suite 3290
Los Angeles, CA 90067

Note to Parents

GIFTED & TALENTED® REFERENCE WORKBOOKS will help develop your child's natural talents and gifts by providing questions and pencil activities to enhance critical and creative thinking skills. These skills of logic and reasoning teach children **how** to think. They are precisely the skills emphasized by teachers of gifted and talented children.

Thinking skills are the skills needed to be able to learn anything at any time. If a child has a grasp of how to think, school success and even success in life will become more assured. In addition, the child will become self-confident as he or she approaches new tasks with the ability to think them through and discover solutions.

GIFTED & TALENTED® REFERENCE WORKBOOKS present these skills in a unique way, combining the basic subject areas of reading, language arts, and math with dictionary skills, map skills, and other reference-book skills. Here are some of the thinking skills you will find:

- Deduction — the ability to reach a logical conclusion by interpreting clues
- Understanding Relationships — the ability to recognize how objects, shapes, and words are similar or dissimilar; to classify and categorize
- Sequencing — the ability to organize events, numbers; to recognize patterns
- Inference — the ability to reach logical conclusions from given or assumed evidence
- Creative Thinking — the ability to generate unique ideas; to compare and contrast the same elements in different situations; to present imaginative solutions to problems

How to Use GIFTED & TALENTED® REFERENCE WORKBOOKS:

Each book contains thinking activities that challenge children. You may need to work with your child on many of the pages, especially with the child who is a nonreader. However, even a nonreader can master thinking skills, and the sooner your child learns how to think, the better. Read the books with your child and, if necessary, explain the activities. Let your child choose to answer the questions or do the activities that interest him or her. When interest wanes, stop. A page or two at a time may be enough, as the child should have fun while learning.

It is important to remember that these activities are designed to teach your child **how to think,** not how to find the right answer. Teachers of gifted children are never surprised when a child discovers a new "right" answer. For example, a child may be asked to choose the object that doesn't belong in this group: a table, a chair, a book, a desk. The best answer is **book,** since all the others are furniture. But a child could respond that all of them belong because they all could be found in an office or a library. The best way to react to this type of response is to praise the child and gently point out that there is another answer, too. While creativity should be encouraged, your child must look for the best and most **suitable** answer.

GIFTED AND TALENTED® REFERENCE WORKBOOKS have been written by teachers. Educationally sound and endorsed by a leader in the gifted field, this series will benefit any child who demonstrates curiosity, imagination, a sense of fun and wonder about the world, and a desire to learn. These books will open your child's mind to new experiences and help fulfill his or her true potential.

WHAT IS AN ALMANAC?

This almanac is about you and your world.

It has lists of things you might like to know about. It has lists of things you might like to do.

You can use this almanac for ideas about what to do any time of year. It can remind you of games you might like to play, alone or with friends. It has lists of books, movies, and television shows. This book has information on animals you might want to learn more about. If you are hungry, there are even foods you can learn how to make!

You can add to this almanac. If your favorite game is not here, add it to a list of your own. If you have a favorite movie, television show, or book that is not here, you can add that to your list, too.

There is even a section on new things for you to learn how to do, like make your own book!

This almanac is your book to use as much as you would like. You can turn to it again and again to learn more. Enjoy it!

THE EARTH

We all live on the planet Earth. The Earth is covered with water (the oceans) and dirt and rocks (the land).

Although you can't tell from where you are, the Earth is round, like an orange. You can see this by looking at pictures of Earth taken from space.

We cannot feel it, but the Earth moves around the Sun. There are nine big, round planets that all move around the Sun. Isn't that surprising?

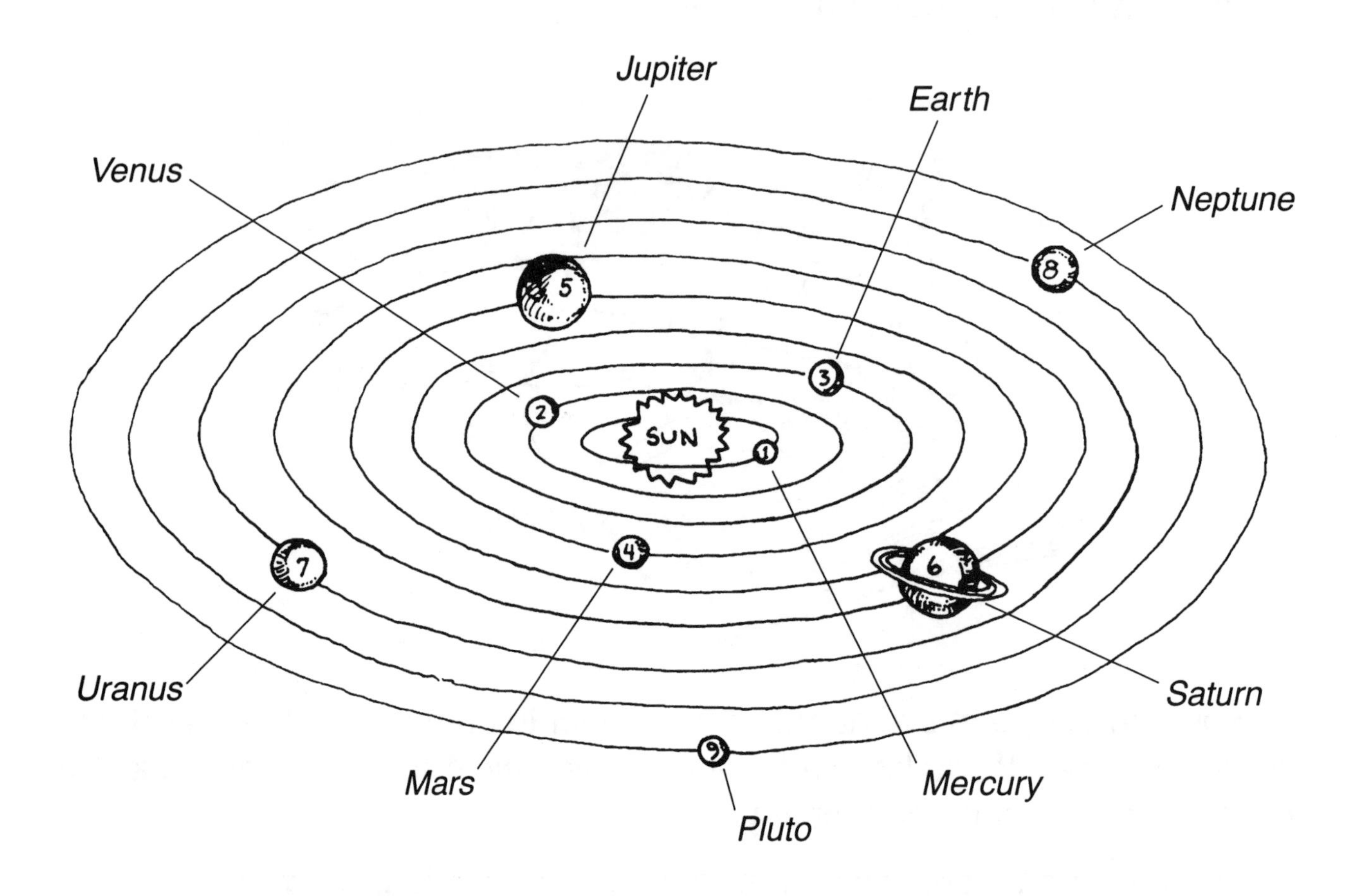

Look at the nine planets in the picture.
Which planet is closest to the Sun?
Which planet is farthest from the Sun?

THE SUN

Every day, as the Earth spins, the Sun comes up in the east and goes down in the west.

The Sun is very, very bright. It gives off its own light. The sunlight makes our days bright, and it makes plants grow.

On some days we cannot see the Sun because the sky is cloudy. But the Sun is always there.

The Sun is also very, very hot. It sends us lots of heat that keeps us warm. Without the Sun, we could not live.

What would happen to these flowers if the Sun didn't shine?
What else do plants need to live?

SUN FACT

*The Sun is a **star**! If that's true, why doesn't it look like a twinkling dot of light, like all the other stars in the sky?*

Because *it* is much *closer* to us.

The Sun's rays provide the energy source for every living thing on Earth. Begin at the center of the Sun and find a path that allows the energy to beam toward Earth.

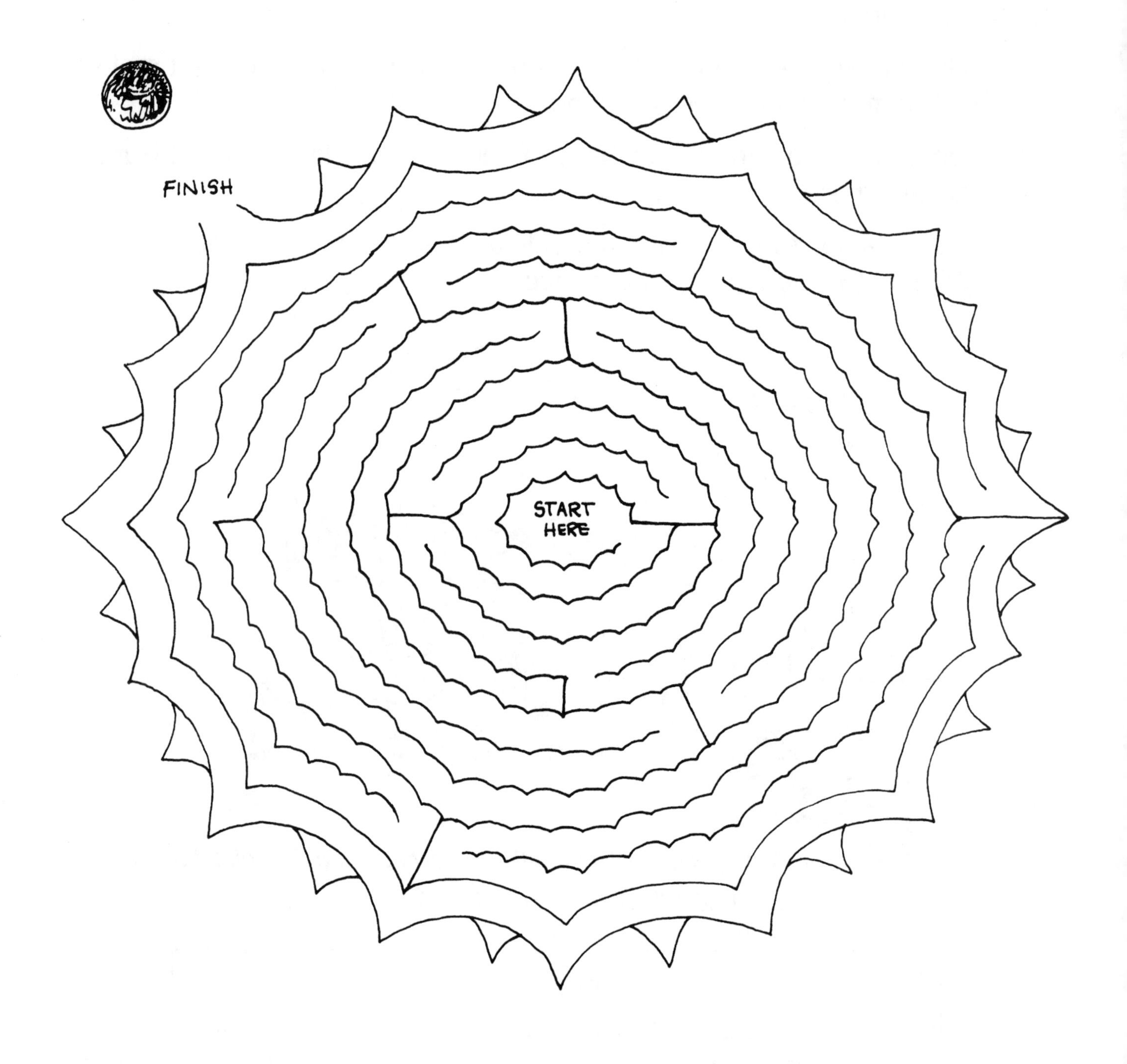

The Sun is the center of our Solar System. The Earth and all the other planets travel around the Sun.

The Sun is made up of gases. Hydrogen makes up most of the Sun, but it also contains a lot of helium. There are small amounts of many other gases.

Use the information on this page and on page 7 to help you complete the crossword puzzle below.

Across

3. The Sun is the center of the ______________ System.
4. The Sun is mostly made of ______________ .
6. The Sun also contains lots of ______________ .

Down

1. The ______________ travel around the Sun.
2. The Sun is a ______________ .
3. This puzzle is about the ______________ .
4. The Sun gives off ______________ .
5. The Sun is the nearest star to ______________ .
7. The Sun makes its own ______________ .

S
U
N

THE MOON

The Moon does not give off its own light. It does not give us heat. We can see the Moon only because it shines back the Sun's light like a mirror.

Sometimes we see the Moon at night, sometimes in the day.

When we see the Moon in the daytime, it does not seem bright at all. But at night the Moon lights up the land.

Several astronauts have been to the Moon. There is no air there to breathe. The astronauts had to wear special protective suits with helmets so that they could breathe and stay warm.

Would you like to go to the Moon? What would you bring with you?

Think of something you could leave on the Moon that would tell future astronauts you had been there.

THE STARS

If you live in the city, you can see a few thousand stars in the night sky. You can see even more in the country, away from bright city lights. But actually there are billions and billions of stars in space. Most of them are just too far away to see.

People who are lost can find their way by looking at the stars. The North Star is roughly above the North Pole, so it tells people which direction is north. You can find the North Star by first finding the Big Dipper, which is a group of stars. The Big Dipper is a part of the constellation called the Big Bear.

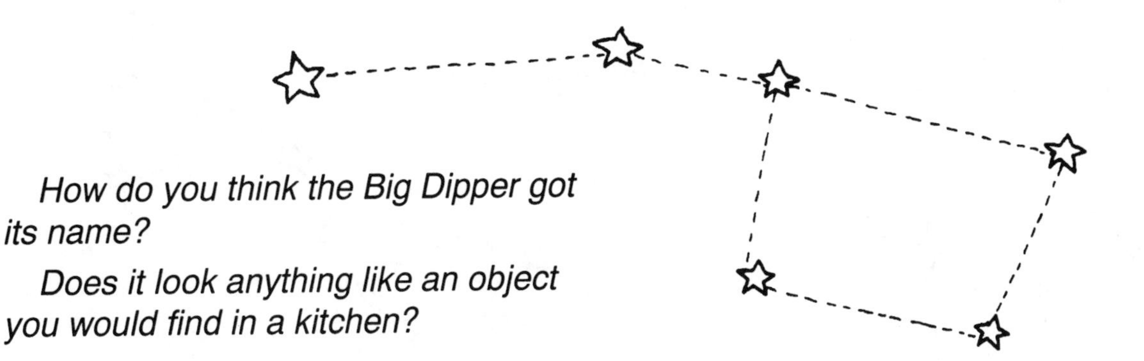

How do you think the Big Dipper got its name?

Does it look anything like an object you would find in a kitchen?

OTHER CONSTELLATIONS

Spring
Draco, the Dragon
Leo, the Lion
Cancer, the Crab

Summer
Cygnus, the Swan
Scorpius, the Scorpion
Sagittarius, the Archer

Autumn
Pegasus, the Winged Horse
Cetus, the Whale
Aries, the Ram

Winter
Orion, the Hunter
Taurus, the Bull
Gemini, the Twins

Look at the pictures of constellations, or groups of stars, below. Match each constellation to the picture on the next page that you think it represents.

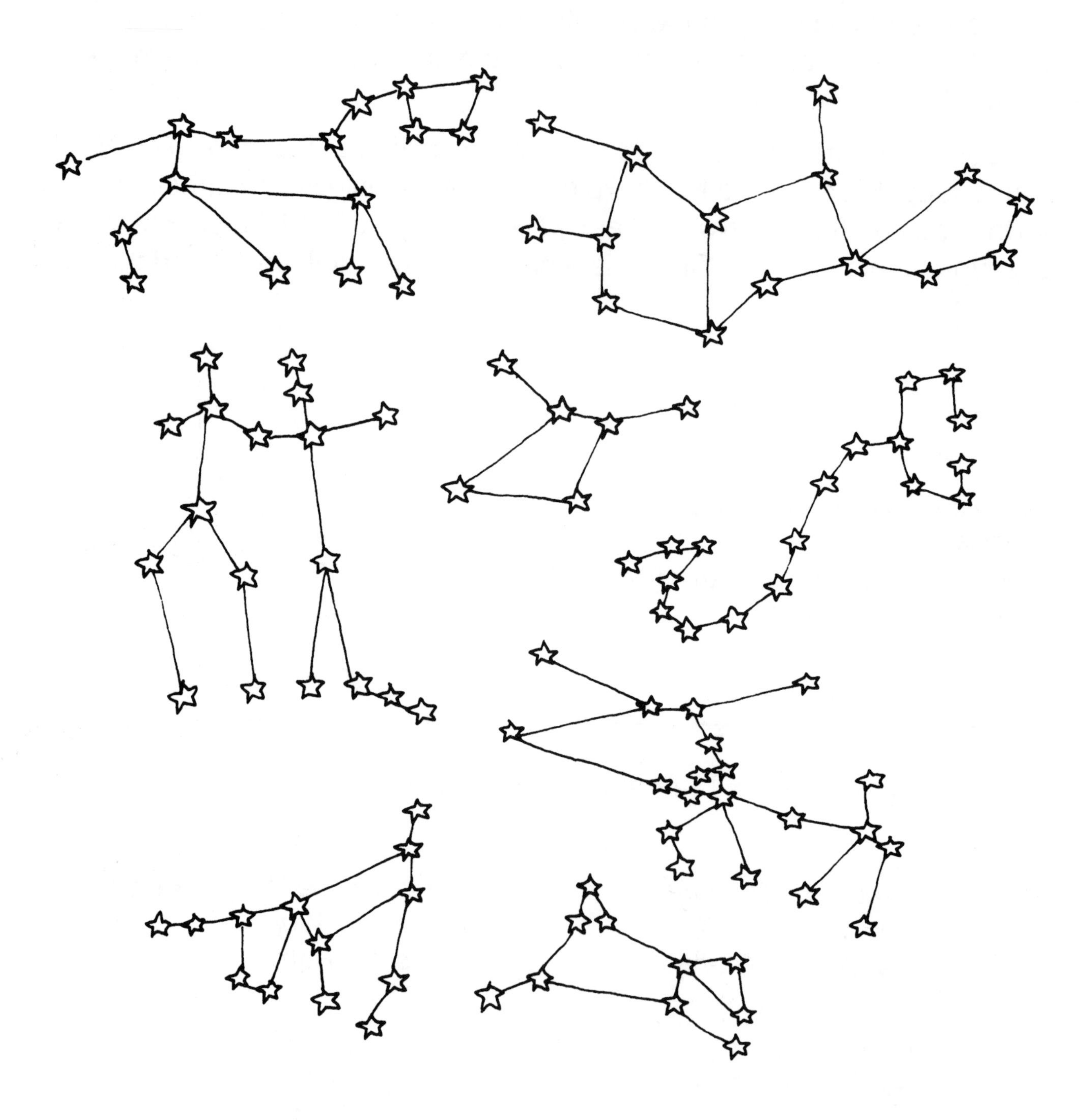

ANIMALS

On planet Earth, we live with many other living things. Some of them are plants and some are animals. Can you think of some different animals you know of?

Animals come in many shapes and sizes, and no one knows how many kinds there are. But we do know that different animals are alike in different ways. For instance, all **fish** live in water. All but a few kinds of **birds** can fly. All **reptiles** have scaly skin. What do you think all **insects** have in common? Legs! Six of them, to be exact.

Although there are millions of different creatures, you can usually tell what *kind* of animal the creature is just by looking at it.

THE FIRST KIND OF ANIMAL:
INSECTS

- *lay eggs*
- *have six legs*
- *nearly all have wings (but that doesn't always mean they can fly)*
- *have a skeleton on the outside of their bodies!*

An **ant** is so small, you would have to lie on your belly to get a good look at it. Ants live in hills with other ants, just like people live in towns with other people. How many legs does an ant have? An ant has six legs. What would *you* do if you had that many legs?

A **bee** has four wings, not just two like birds do. Bees live with other bees in cities called hives. They do not use sounds to speak. Bees "talk" to one another by dancing.

A **butterfly** is larger than a bee, but like a bee, it has four wings. A butterfly starts as a caterpillar with many legs, then it becomes a butterfly.

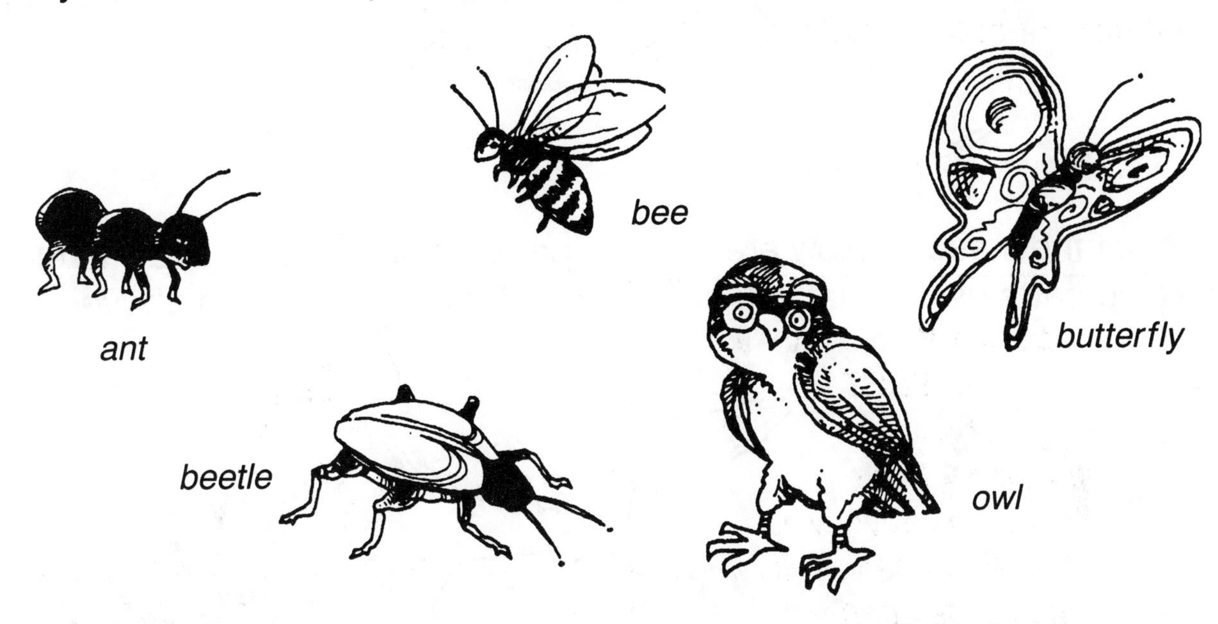

Which of these animals is not an insect? Why?

What kind of animal is it?

Insects with Four Wings

- *bee*
- *wasp*
- *fly*
- *dragonfly*
- *moth*
- *cricket*
- *grasshopper*
- *some beetles*
- *ladybug*

Here is a diagram of an insect. Look at it carefully.

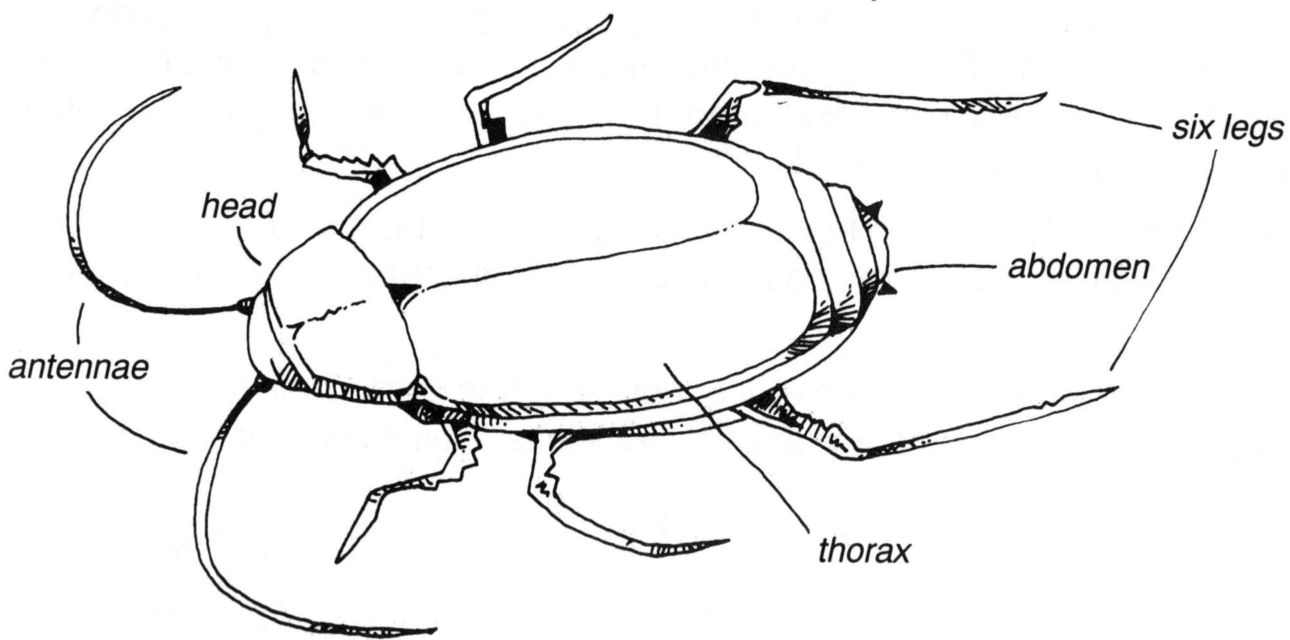

All of the insects below are missing parts of their bodies. Draw in the missing parts using what you have learned from the diagram above.

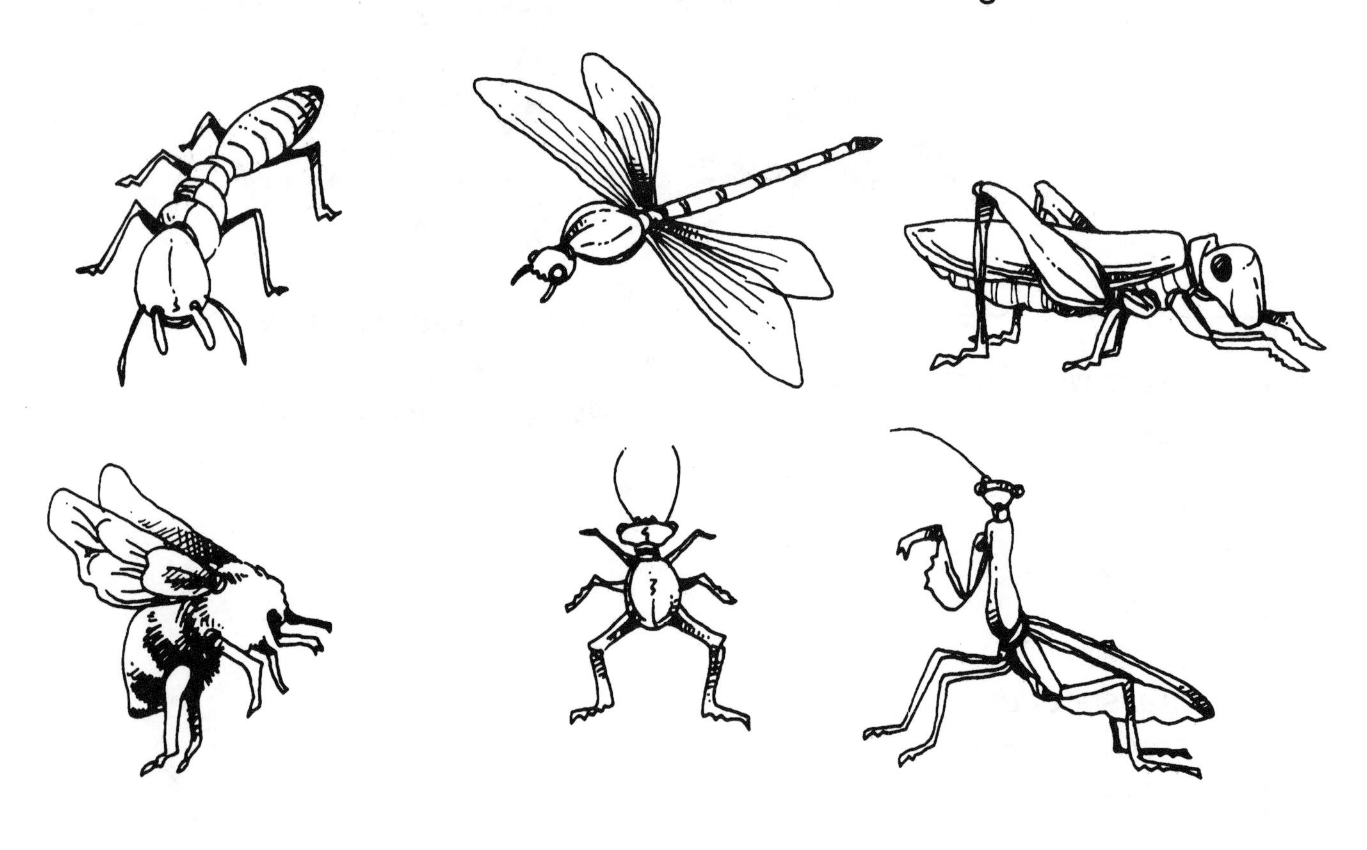

Many insects go through amazing changes during their lifetimes. A butterfly begins life as a tiny egg laid on a leaf. The egg hatches, and a tiny caterpillar emerges. The caterpillar begins to eat and grow. When it has grown large enough, the caterpillar spins a cocoon around itself. Inside the cocoon, the caterpillar changes into a butterfly. Then the butterfly nibbles a hole in the cocoon and comes out to spread its wings.

Number the pictures below in the correct order, from 1 to 6, using the information you have learned above.

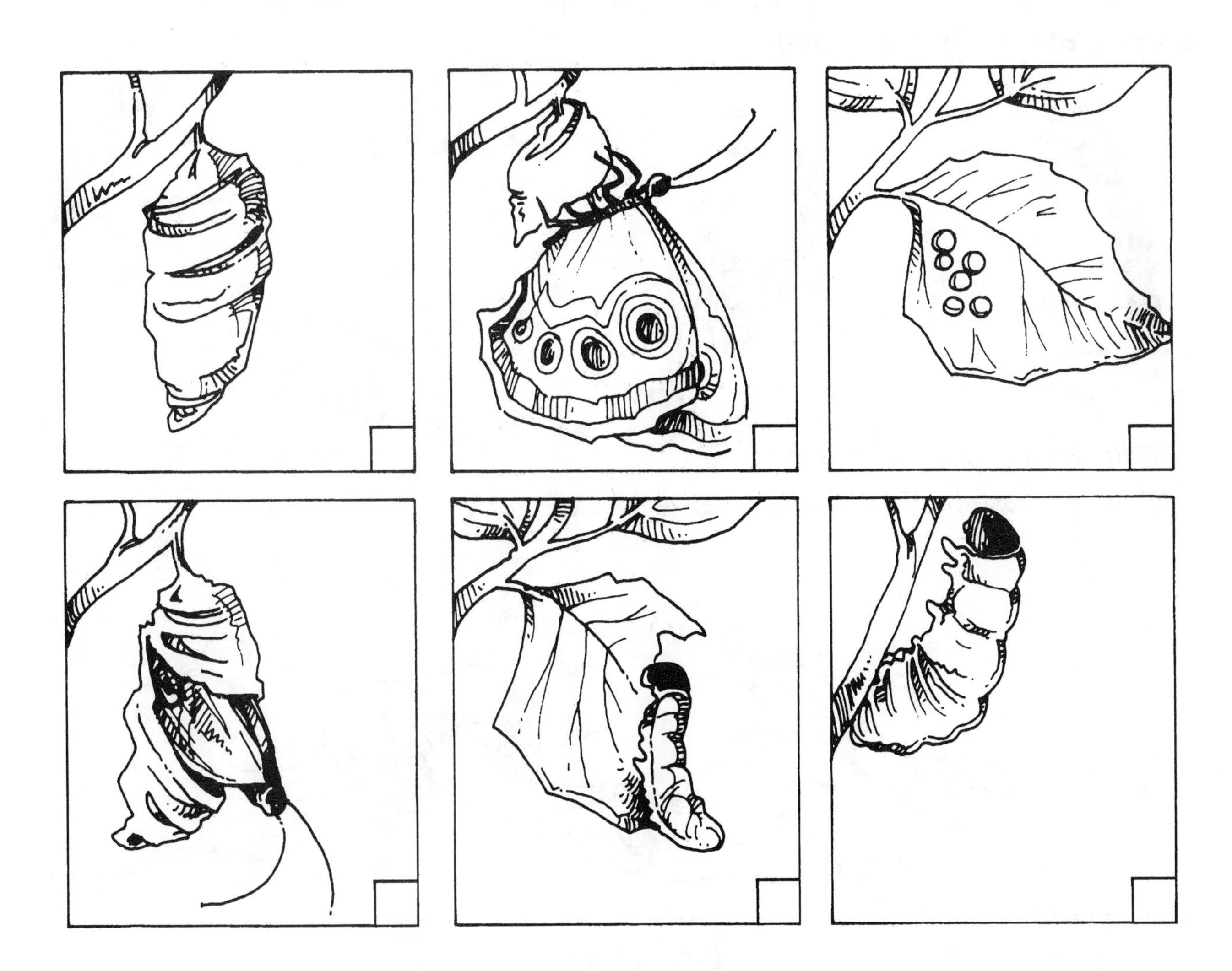

A **hummingbird** can fly, just like a butterfly can. A hummingbird is the smallest bird. It is so small that some butterflies are actually bigger than it! But hummingbirds are much better fliers. They fly so fast, you can hardly see their wings move.

An **ostrich** is the biggest bird. It lives in the grasslands of Africa. It cannot fly, but it can run—and *fast,* too. An ostrich can run faster than an Olympic racer.

THE SECOND KIND OF ANIMAL:
BIRDS

- *lay eggs*
- *have feathers*
- *have two wings*
- *have two legs*
- *nearly always build nests*
- *can nearly always fly*

penguin

eagle

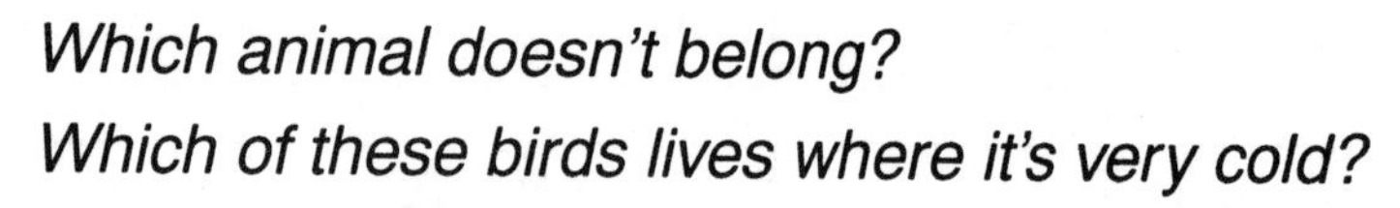
Which animal doesn't belong?
Which of these birds lives where it's very cold?

BIG AND SMALL

An ostrich is as heavy as two grown-ups put together!
A hummingbird weighs less than a pencil.
Which is bigger, an eagle or an ostrich? A robin or a hummingbird?

Birds all hatch from eggs. There are as many different kinds of eggs as there are birds. Eggs can be as small as a jelly bean or as large as a grapefruit!

Draw a line from each bird to its shell, using the clues below.

- The first bird did not hatch out of the striped egg.
- The last bird did not hatch out of the plain egg.
- The middle bird is the largest bird.

A **lizard** is a fast runner, too, but it's not anything like an ostrich! What kind of animal is it? There are lots of kinds of lizards. They each have four legs for scooting along the ground very fast. Lizards have scaly skin.

Snakes have scaly skin, too. In fact, they're a lot like lizards, except they don't have legs! They move their bodies by sliding them back and forth along the ground. The littlest snake is about as long as your hand. The biggest snake is as long as a house!

THE THIRD KIND OF ANIMAL:

REPTILES

How are a lizard, snake, turtle, and alligator alike? They're all reptiles. Nearly all reptiles:

- *lay eggs*
- *have scaly skin*
- *have four legs (except snakes, which have no legs)*
- *build nests*

Which animal does not belong?

How is a snake like a worm?

Like lizards and snakes, **turtles** also have scaly skin. But their scales are *big,* and they form a hard shell that is like a house. Turtles spend most of their time in the water.

There are other kinds of animals that spend a lot of time in the water. Besides fish, can you think of one? How about a **frog**? Frogs can really hop! They have strong back legs so they can hop all along the bank of a stream or a lake.

THE FOURTH KIND OF ANIMAL:

AMPHIBIANS

- *lay eggs*
- *begin life underwater, breathing through gills*
- *eventually grow legs and come ashore, breathing air*
- *have either smooth, moist skin (frogs, salamanders) or rough, dry skin (toads)*

Which of these animals lives in the water?

Which are not amphibians?

Fish live their whole lives in water. They eat in water and breathe in water. Some fish are so tiny you can barely see them. Other fish are very big. A **shark** is a very big fish. Some sharks are as long as a bus!

Some fish, like **angelfish** or **zebra fish,** have pretty stripes or spots.

octopus

THE FIFTH KIND OF ANIMAL:

FISH

- *lay eggs*
- *live in water*
- *have fins for swimming*
- *nearly all have scaly skin*
- *breathe through gills*

goldfish

angelfish

lobster

clam

shark

All these animals live in the sea, but they're not all fish. Which are not fish? Why?

Do you think you could eat underwater? What would it be like?

Would you have to hold on to your plate?

There are many different kinds of fish. Some live in the salty water of the ocean. Others life in freshwater, such as lakes, rivers, and streams. Find the names of the fish listed below in the word search. Remember that the words may be found from right to left, left to right, or up and down.

TROUT	**LOACH**	**MARLIN**	**SAILFISH**
SALMON	**ANGELFISH**	**POMPANO**	**SWORDFISH**
BASS	**FLOUNDER**	**BLUEFISH**	**MACKEREL**
GUPPY	**TUNA**	**SHARK**	**HADDOCK**

P	E	R	B	L	U	E	F	I	S	H	S
O	N	A	A	L	C	E	N	R	T	I	E
M	A	T	S	E	P	M	E	D	W	R	G
T	F	H	S	W	O	R	D	F	I	S	H
U	S	F	J	W	M	O	T	I	D	A	M
O	W	Y	X	Z	P	L	Q	B	Z	L	E
R	G	N	S	H	A	R	K	H	V	M	U
T	U	N	A	C	N	R	T	B	Y	O	F
J	W	I	K	C	O	D	D	A	H	N	L
O	Q	L	F	S	C	V	B	N	C	A	O
W	E	R	T	Y	U	I	O	S	A	S	U
F	S	A	I	L	F	I	S	H	O	G	N
M	N	M	A	C	K	E	R	E	L	P	D
I	U	Y	G	U	P	P	Y	T	R	E	E
A	S	H	S	I	F	L	E	G	N	A	R

Find out more about these fish by looking in an encyclopedia. Can you guess from their names what some of them might look like?

An **octopus** lives in the sea, too, but it's not a fish. It's a kind of **mollusk**. An octopus has eight arms! How many people would you hug if *you* had eight arms?

A **clam** lives in water and is a kind of mollusk, too. It has two hard shells that snap together. One kind of clam is as big as your hand. Another kind is as wide as you are tall!

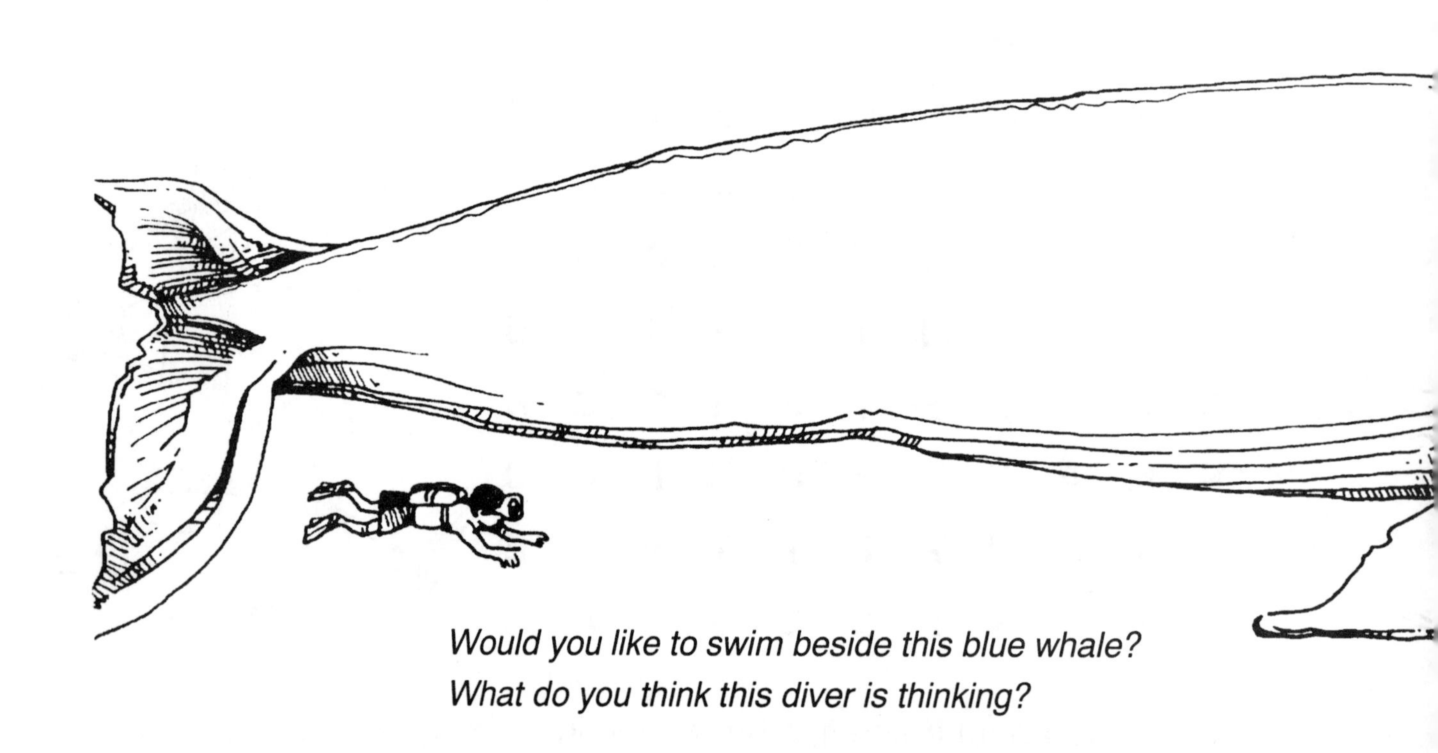

Would you like to swim beside this blue whale? What do you think this diver is thinking?

Whales live in the sea, but they are *not* mollusks and they are *not* fish. In fact, though it may be hard to believe, they are a lot like *you*! Whales are **mammals.** Whales care for their babies, like your mother cared for you when you were young.

Whales are big! They can be as small as a car, or as big as three buses! The **blue whale** is the biggest, heaviest animal on land or sea.

Sea Mammals

- *whales*
- *seals*
- *dolphins*
- *porpoises*
- *sea lions*
- *walruses*
- *manatees*
- *otters*

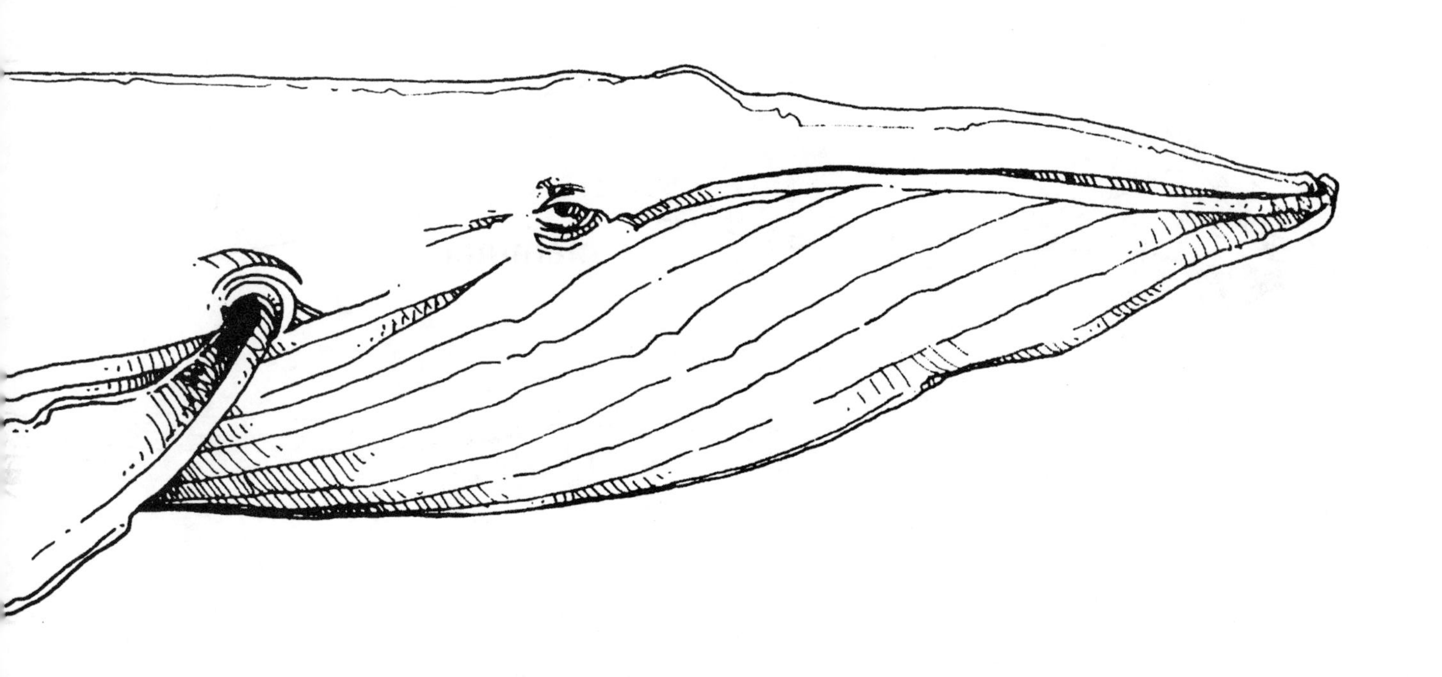

How many words can you think of that have the same meaning as **big**? Write them on the lines below.

______________ ______________ ______________

______________ ______________ ______________

Use your words from this page and the next to complete the outline of the whale. This is called a **concrete poem**. The words that make up the poem take the shape of the thing that the poem is about.

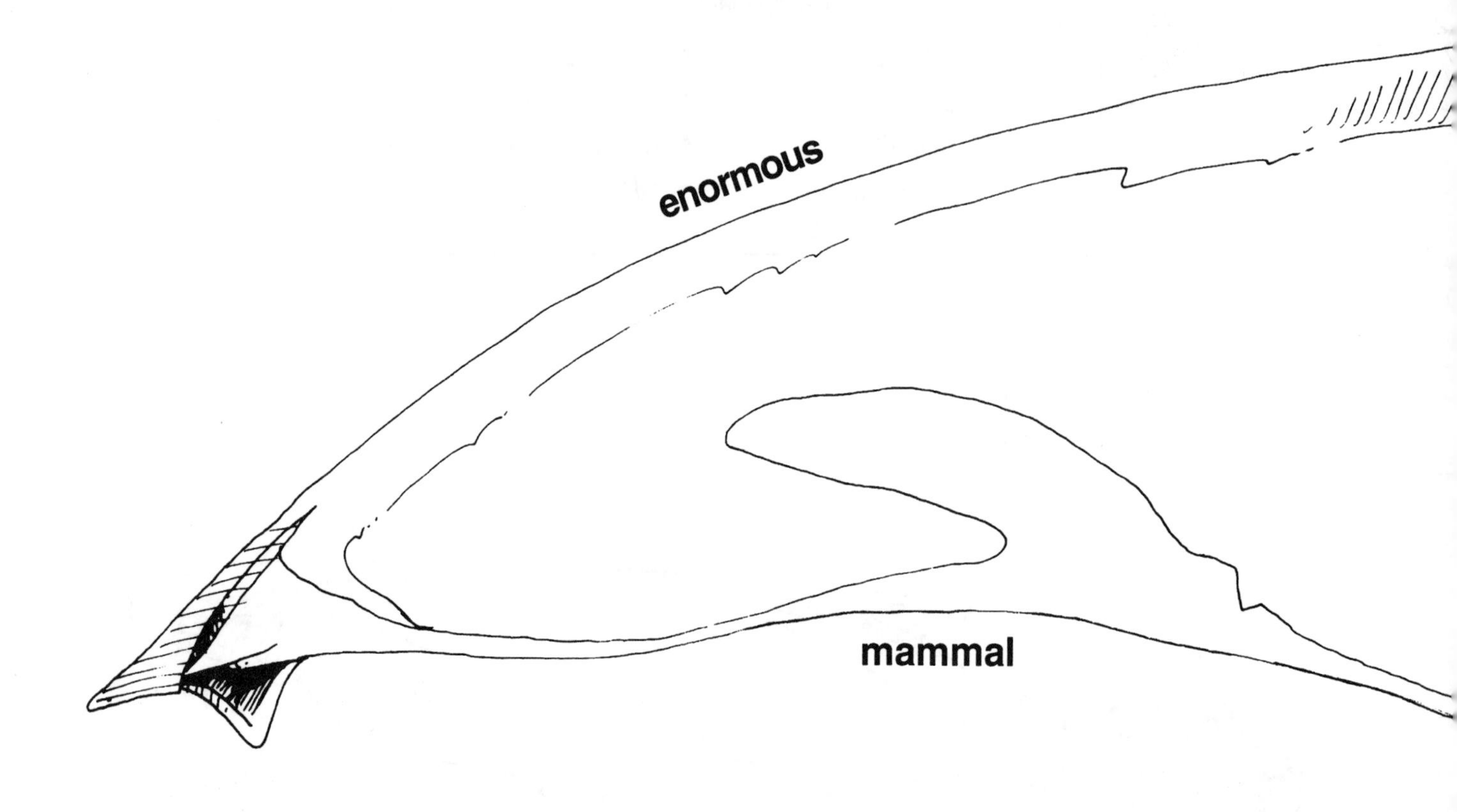

What other words can you use to describe, or tell about, whales? Write them on the lines below.

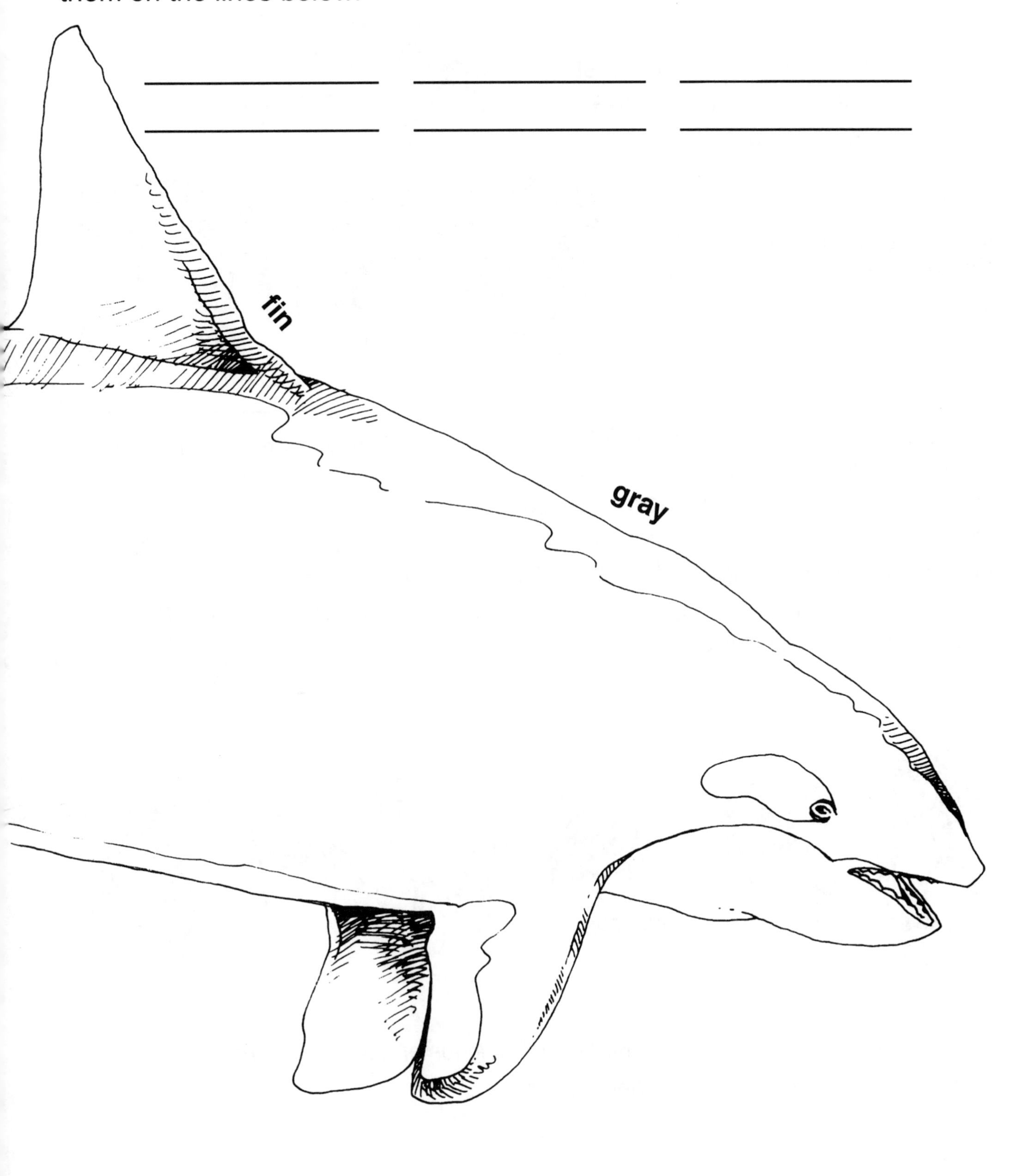

Most mammals don't live in the sea—they live on land. They come in all shapes and sizes. One kind of mammal can even fly!

A **mouse** is one of the smallest mammals. Mice sleep during the day and eat breakfast at night! How would you like to do that? If you ate as much for your size as a mouse does, you would have to eat twenty loaves of bread a day!

A **squirrel** is bigger than a mouse. A **fox** is bigger than a squirrel. A **wolf** is bigger than a fox. A **person** is bigger than a wolf. A **horse** is bigger than a person. A **camel** is bigger than a horse. And an **elephant** is the biggest mammal of all—on land, that is!

THE SIXTH KIND OF ANIMAL:
MAMMALS

- *have hair or fur*
- *usually have four limbs*
- *breathe air*
- *give birth to living babies*
- *feed milk to their babies*

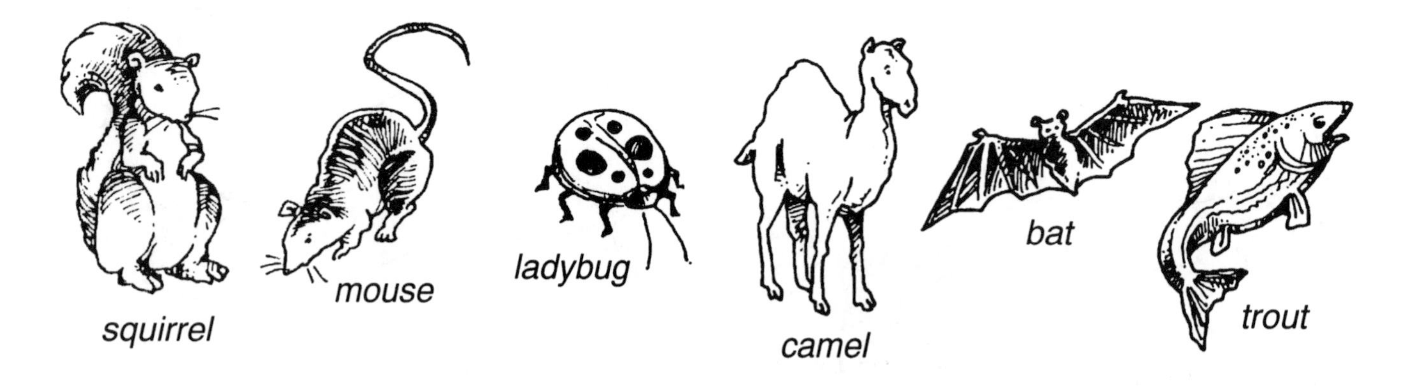

Which animals here are not mammals? What kinds of animals are they?
Which of the mammals shown here can fly?

DINOSAURS

Dinosaurs lived a very long time ago. Some dinosaurs ate meat and some ate plants. The dinosaurs were different sizes. What kinds of animals do you think dinosaurs were? They were reptiles.

Tyrannosaurus (tie-ran-o-SAWR-us) was as tall as a two-story house and about as long. It was heavier than your family and friends put together! With its huge teeth in its big head, *Tyrannosaurus* ate other dinosaurs.

The dinosaur *Seismosaurus* (size-mo-SAWR-us) shook the ground when it walked. *Seismosaurus* was taller than your school and heavier than twenty elephants! *Seismosaurus* stretched its long neck to eat pine needles.

What do you think this boy is saying to the Seismosaurus*?*

The dinosaur *Triceratops* (try-SAIR-uh-tops) had three horns on its face and a fancy collar, too. Lots of *Triceratops* lived together in big herds.

The flying dinosaur *Quetzalcoatlus* (ket-zal-co-AT-lus) was as big as a small airplane.

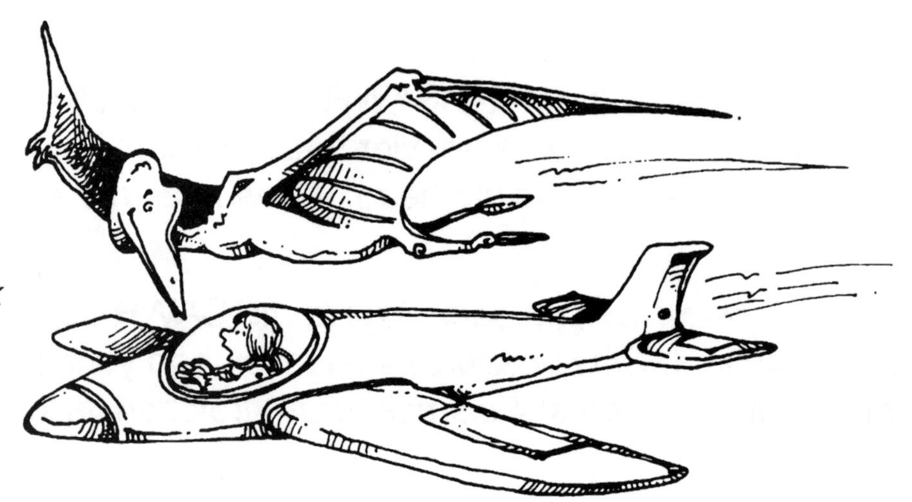

What do you think the pilot is saying?

Some dinosaurs, like *Maiasaura* (my-uh-SAWR-uh) and *Coelophysis* (see-lo-FY-sus), hopped like grasshoppers.

Maiasaura dinosaurs lived with their mothers in little towns. *Coelophysis* dinosaurs lived in flocks, like sheep, with other dinosaurs just like them.

What is your favorite dinosaur?

The dinosaurs disappeared a long, long time ago, but people have found their bones. Would you like to hunt for dinosaur bones? Where would you look for them?

Complete the **acrostic puzzle** below by writing a dinosaur's name across each letter. Remember that the name you choose must contain that letter. The first one has been done for you. If you need help, use the Word Bank at the bottom of the page.

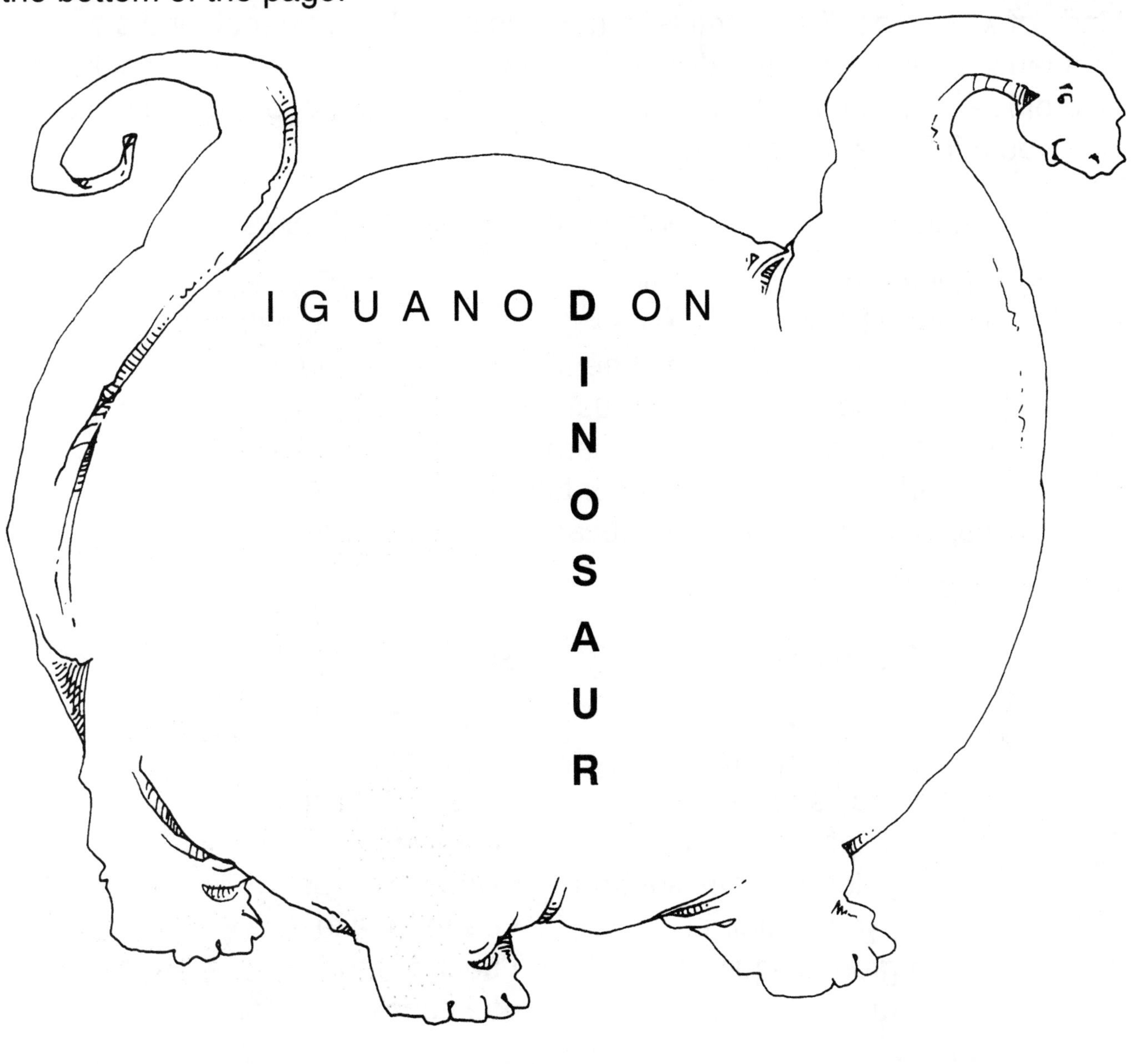

Word Bank:

- APATOSAURUS
- ANKYLOSAURUS
- DIPLODOCUS
- STEGOSAURUS
- ORNITHOMIMUS
- BRACHIOSAURUS
- TRICERATOPS
- DEINONYCHUS
- TYRANNOSAURUS

ANIMAL GROUPS

Now you've learned all about different kinds of animals. But there are kinds of kinds, too! For example, a horse is a kind of mammal, and an Arabian is a kind of horse. Also, a lizard is a kind of reptile, and a gecko is a kind of lizard. There are lots of animal groups on this page and the next. Can you think of any more?

Bears

- polar bear
- grizzly bear
- Kodiak bear
- brown bear
- black bear
- panda
- spectacled bear
- sun bear

Wildcats

- lion
- tiger
- cheetah
- jaguar
- leopard
- mountain lion
- bobcat
- margay

Horses

- Clydesdale
- Appaloosa
- quarterhorse
- Shetland pony
- thoroughbred
- Morgan
- palomino
- Welsh pony

Squirrels

- red squirrel
- flying squirrel
- gray squirrel
- chipmunk
- golden mantle squirrel
- pygmy squirrel
- ground squirrel
- marmot

Snakes

- rattlesnake
- tree snake
- boa constrictor
- coral snake
- water moccasin
- garter snake
- boomslang
- sea snake

Primates

- monkey
- chimpanzee
- gorilla
- orangutan
- lemur
- baboon
- gibbon
- marmoset

Butterflies

- monarch butterfly
- cabbage butterfly
- tortoiseshell
- painted lady
- red admiral
- mourning cloak
- Apollo
- regent skipper

Ants

- wood ant
- honeypot ant
- parasol ant
- driver ant
- army ant
- harvesting ant
- fire ant
- leaf-cutting ant

Lizards

- horned lizard
- gecko
- iguana
- Gila monster
- bearded lizard
- frilled lizard
- flying dragon
- Komodo dragon

You belong to one of these animal groups. Do you know which one?

How are all the wildcats alike? How are they different? (You can see some pictures of wildcats on page 40.)

What do all ants have that is the same?

Animals sometimes live together in groups. These groups have special names. Draw a line from each animal name below to the name of its group.

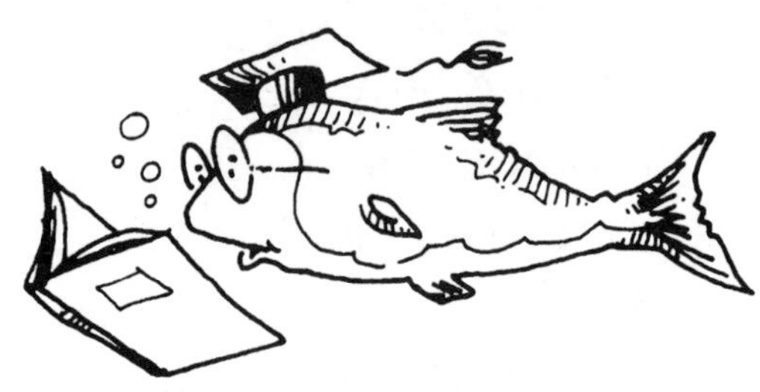

buffalo	gaggle
fish	pod
goose	school
lion	flock
whale	herd
pigeon	pride

(Answers: buffalo → herd; fish → school; goose → gaggle; lion → pride; whale → pod; pigeon → flock)

There are special names for animal babies, too. Draw a line from each animal to its baby. Fill in the correct baby names for each! Use the Word Bank if you need help.

Word Bank:

gosling	bear	dog	kitten
cow	calf	chick	puppy
cub	hen	goose	
horse	cat	colt	

Dogs

Some **dogs,** like wolves and foxes, are wild. But most dogs are domestic. That means that they live with us as pets. All dogs bark or howl, and they have noses that can smell things we cannot. Dogs come in all sizes, from little to big.

The littlest pet dog is a **Chihuahua** (chee-WAH-wah). A Chihuahua has almost no hair. The heaviest pet dog is the **Saint Bernard,** and the **Great Dane** is the tallest one.

Do you know these famous dogs from movies, television shows, and books? Can you name any others?

- Huckleberry Hound
- Goofy
- Toto
- Rin Tin Tin
- White Fang
- Lassie
- Snoopy
- Scooby-Doo
- Beethoven

Dogs, Dogs, and More Dogs

- *Scottish terrier*
- *golden retriever*
- *Labrador retriever*
- *Irish setter*
- *beagle*
- *basset hound*
- *schnauzer*
- *poodle*
- *Welsh corgi*
- *German shepherd*
- *collie*
- *cocker spaniel*

Some dogs work for a living. There are many jobs that they do.

Guard dogs keep robbers away. Dogs like this **Doberman pinscher** are often used to guard property.

Herding dogs keep sheep and cows together and stop them from straying. These dogs are very smart.

This **sheepdog** is a common type of herding dog.

Police dogs have a keen sense of smell. They help the police department capture criminals and solve crimes.

This **German shepherd** would make a very good police dog.

Rescue dogs find people lost in the snow or in dangerous places. Many rescue dogs are big, strong Saint Bernards.

Seeing-eye dogs help blind people find their way around.

Labrador retrievers like this one are common seeing-eye dogs.

Hearing-ear dogs help deaf people hear. The dogs can tell when someone is at the door, if the phone is ringing, or if a fire alarm is sounding.

This **cocker spaniel** would be a good hearing-ear dog.

Astronaut dogs have ridden in spaceships. In fact, the first animal in space was not a person but a dog!

Can you think of other jobs that dogs can do?

You have read about many different kinds of dogs. Find the names of the dogs below in the word search. Remember that the words may be found from right to left, left to right, or up and down.

BEAGLE	CHIHUAHUA	DACHSHUND	SCHNAUZER
DOBERMAN	GREYHOUND	POODLE	GREAT DANE
BOXER	COLLIE	SHEEPDOG	BULLDOG
COCKER SPANIEL	BASSET HOUND	IRISH SETTER	WELSH CORGI

D F H J L N P R S V W Y A Z B K
C X D R L M O A P N E K J I T C
C B E A G L E O P G L S T E A H
D A C H S H U N D R S C K E N R
A S T D I R E C S E H S T U D E
T S D I R E C S T Y C O R Y D E
V E R B R O N H C H O O S J O E
N T E L W A Y E P O R Q U A R N
E H R B A I C E K U G L S U P A
C O C K E R S P A N I E L B C D
R U B O W I C D L D N L I N E T
Y N F O G S H O U R S D E V E A
T D Y P O H N G E R L O E N T E
A S S C D S A M P L E O T I O R
S A L M L E U O S T N P O E I G
T E R C L T Z E R E X O B I P T
O N S W U T E I L L R O N L I N
B U D O B E R M A N N C H L O F
O U C H D R O W N S T W O O P O
N T C O N A U H A U H I H C V E

Cats

There are many kinds of **cats**, both big and small. Domestic, or pet, cats are the smallest cats. They live in their owners' homes. Wildcats are the largest cats.

Cats can see at night, and they walk very quietly. They have claws they can hide in their paws.

You can see wildcats in circuses and zoos.

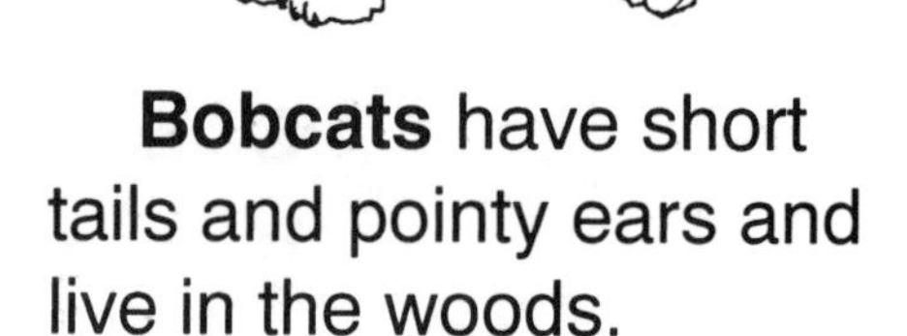

Bobcats have short tails and pointy ears and live in the woods.

Tigers have black stripes and live in the forest.

Lions are light brown and live in grasslands. A lion has a long mane that is like your hair.

Cheetahs have spots and live in dry grasslands. Cheetahs run as fast as cars drive on the road. If a cheetah lived in a city, a police officer would have to give the cheetah a ticket for speeding!

Pet cats have soft fur on their bodies and whiskers on their faces. When they are happy, pet cats purr. This is a soft rattling sound that you can hear when you are close to them. A pet cat will sometimes purr if you stroke its fur, rub it behind the ears, or rub it under its neck.

Pet Cats Aplenty

- *tortoiseshell*
- *Siamese*
- *Burmese*
- *tabby*
- *Manx*
- *shorthair*
- *Persian*
- *Maine coon*
- *Abyssinian*
- *Himalayan*
- *calico*
- *Russian blue*

How are these pet cats alike?
How are they different?

Do you know these famous cats from movies, television shows, and books? Do you know any others?

- The Cowardly Lion
- Garfield
- Tigger
- The Cat in the Hat
- Bagheera
- Puss in Boots
- Hobbes
- Felix

We sometimes use the words "cat" and "dog" to mean more than just the animals. Do you know any of these expressions?

Cat Talk

- *catty-cornered* **on opposite corners**
- *cat burglar* **a thief who is very quiet**
- *catnap* **a quick sleep**
- *scaredy-cat* **a person who is frightened**
- *cattail* **a plant**

Dog Talk

- *dogcart* **a small cart**
- *dog days* **the hot part of summer**
- *dog paddle* **a simple way to swim**
- *dogwood* **a tree**
- *dog-eared* **ragged**
- *dog tag* **a metal nametag that dogs and soldiers wear**

If you could have *any* animal for a pet, what would it be? A tiger? A camel?

How would you take care of your pet? What would you feed it?

How would you play with it?

Other Common Pets

- *turtle*
- *fish*
- *guinea pig*
- *lizard*
- *horse*
- *mouse*
- *snake*
- *hamster*
- *bird*
- *rabbit*

Which of these pets are kept in cages? Which pet is kept in a barn? Which pets are kept in a tank?

Animals are not able to speak our language, but they all have their own ways of being heard. Fill in the bubbles with the words that the animals might use to have a conversation. Use the Word Bank if you need help.

Word Bank:	neigh	oink	woof	meow
	quack	cackle	growl	purr
	baa	squawk	grunt	squeal
	snort	yip	moo	cluck

Famous Animals

Do you know these famous animals from movies, television shows, and books? What kinds of animals are they? Can you name any others?

- The Black Stallion
- Pegasus
- Babar
- Dumbo
- Yogi Bear
- Smokey the Bear
- Eeyore
- Gummi Bears
- Mama Bear, Papa Bear, and Baby Bear
- Jumbo
- Mister Ed
- Winnie-the-Pooh
- Paddington
- Black Beauty
- Benji
- Gentle Ben
- Horton

Animal Toys

When you were younger, did you have any of these animal toys? Can you name any others?

- rocking horse
- turtle rattle
- stuffed or plastic dinosaur
- teddy bear
- rubber duck

What animal toys do you have now? Which one is your favorite?

On a piece of paper, draw a picture of some of your animal toys.

Animal Movies

Which of these animal movies have you seen?

- *Doctor Doolittle*
- *Watership Down*
- *Lassie Come Home*
- *Black Beauty*
- *Benji*
- *Never Cry Wolf*
- *The Lion King*
- *Teenage Mutant Ninja Turtles*
- *Charlotte's Web*
- *101 Dalmatians*
- *Dumbo*
- *Beethoven*
- *The Jungle Book*
- *Homeward Bound*

Which movie was your favorite? Why?

Animal Songs

Do you know any of these animal songs? Perhaps you can sing one now!

- "Old MacDonald Had a Farm"
- "Three Blind Mice"
- "Eensy Weensy Spider"
- "Thousand-Legged Worm"
- "Farmer in the Dell"

Do you know what happens after the spider is washed out of the spout?

Animal Poems

Read the animal poems on this page and the next. Fill in the blanks to complete the poems in your own way.

The elephant is tall and wide.

He's big enough for ______________ to ride.

His ears are big, his skin is gray.

I wonder if he likes to ______________ .

A spider spins and a spider weaves

Her sticky web among the ______________

To catch a yummy ______________ to eat.

For her, it must be quite a treat!

Through the ocean's foamy spray

Dolphins glide and ______________ and play.

Over waves that crest and crash,

Dolphins leap and dip and ______________ .

Little frog so ______________ and green,

What have your big eyes just seen?

As you ______________ up at the sky,

Are you watching out for flies?

Snakes must slither through the grass

So we can't hear them as they

______________ .

Even though they have no ______________ ,

They're quick to find some food to eat!

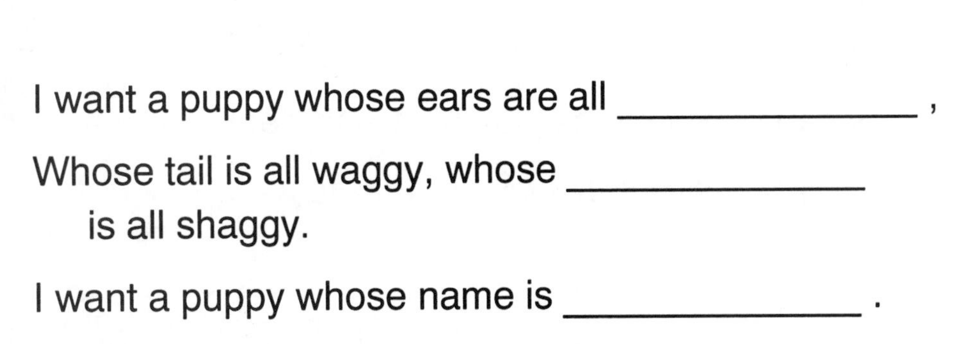

I want a puppy whose ears are all ______________ ,

Whose tail is all waggy, whose ______________ is all shaggy.

I want a puppy whose name is ______________ .

I want a puppy to keep for my own.

Animal Jokes

Here are some animal jokes. Do you know any others?

How did the mouse talk to the elephant?

He used BIG WORDS.

What time is it when twenty cats chase two cats?

Twenty after two.

Why was the mother horse sent to the doctor?

Because she had a little "colt."

Why can't Dalmatians play hide-and-seek?

Because they're always spotted.

Animal Stories

Have you read any of these animal stories? Which one was your favorite? Was it about a character that you like?

- *Bambi*
- *The House at Pooh Corner*
- *Charlotte's Web*
- *The Tale of Peter Rabbit*
- *Goldilocks and the Three Bears*
- *The Cricket in Times Square*
- *The Three Billy Goats Gruff*
- *Yertle the Turtle*
- *The Little Red Hen*
- *The Fox in Sox*

An Animal Quiz

Can you complete the sentences below? Say the missing animal names out loud. You can use the animal pictures to help you choose the names.

I like to play leap______________.

I have a ______________neck sweater.

When I play softball, I hit the ball with a ______________.

I like to eat a hot______________ at the ballpark.

Some girls wear their hair in ______________tails.

Airplanes ______________ high in the sky.

I get a stomachache when I make a ______________ of myself.

When my sister frightened me, she called me a scaredy-______________.

Animal Fun

If you could be any animal, what would you be? Where would you live? What would you do? Draw a picture of the animal and its home in the space below.

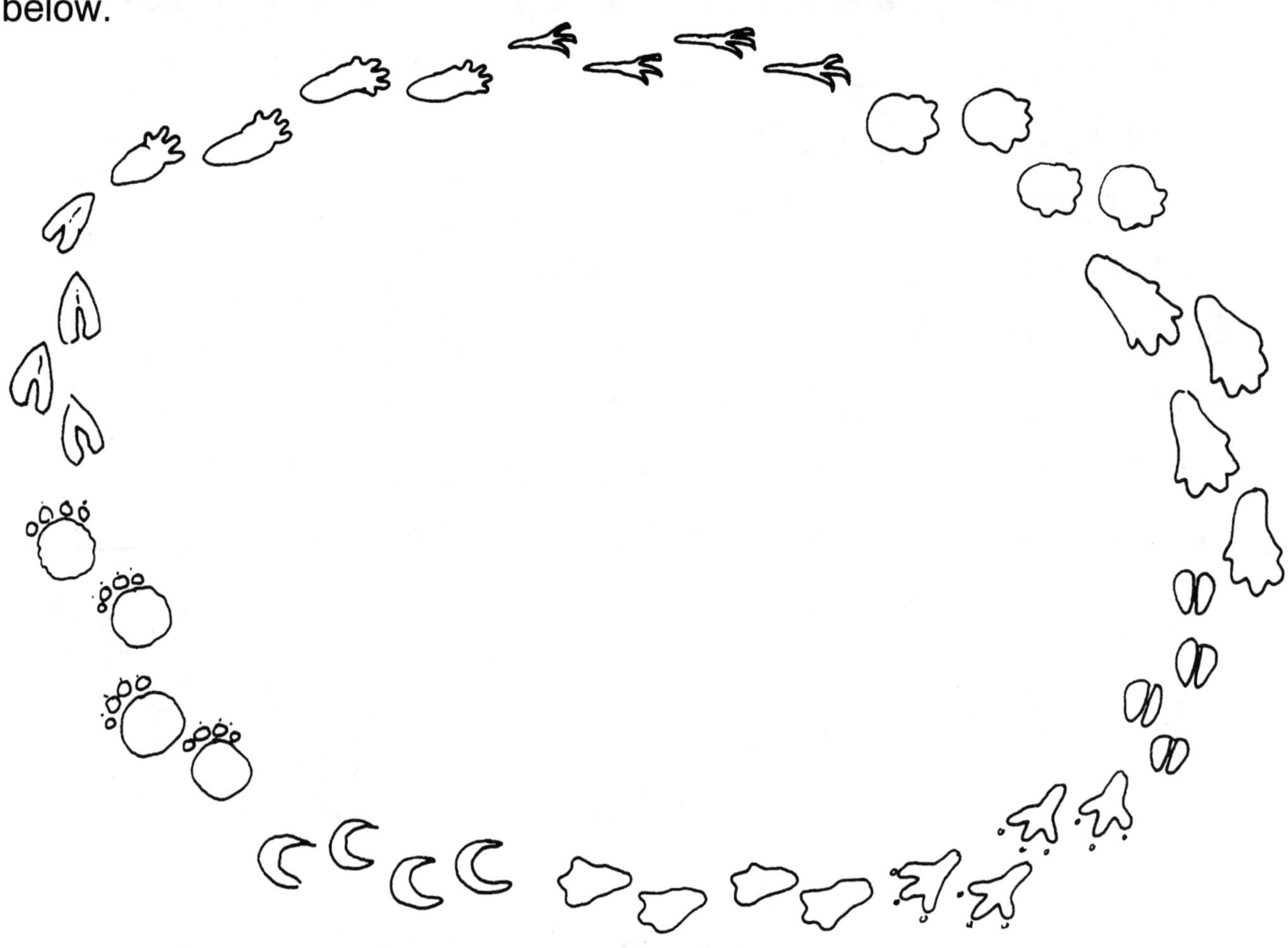

Use the lines to write a sentence or two about the animal you have chosen. Tell why you might like to be this animal.

Fill in the missing letters to find out where these animals all live.

Where do you live? In the space below, draw a picture of your home.

YOU AND YOUR BODY

Mammals have fur, birds have feathers, and fish and reptiles have scales. You are an animal, too, but you have skin covering your body. How well do you know the parts of your body?

Body Parts

Look at the list of words. Point to each body part in the picture.

finger	*ankle*
mouth	*elbow*
lip	*leg*
nose	*teeth*
head	*arm*
toe	*eye*
knee	*hand*
shoulder	*chest*
hip	*stomach*
ear	*neck*
hair	*foot*
bone	*skin*

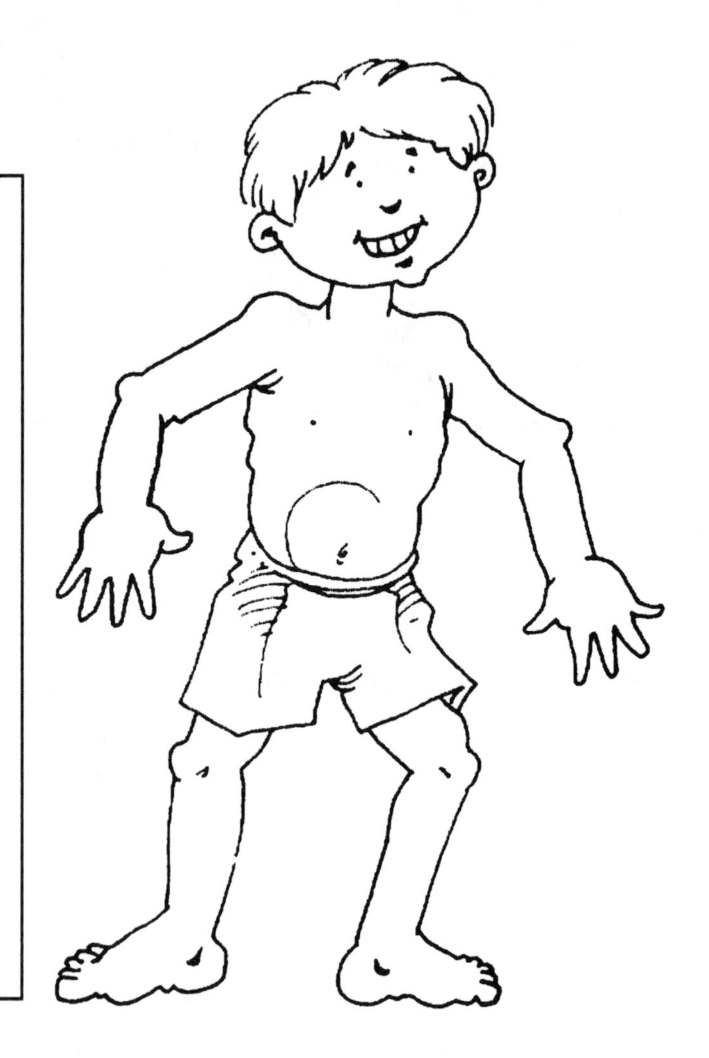

Look at the words in the box. Where on your body would you put them?

shoe	***pants***	***hat***	***glove***	***glasses***
sweater	***scarf***	***shirt***	***sock***	***mitten***

What's wrong with this picture? The girl needs your help to get dressed!

Here is a body joke. Do you know any others?

Why didn't the ghost go to the Halloween party?

Because he had no "body" to go with.

Body Sounds

Try to follow the pattern below using the parts of your body to make movements and sound. Create a steady beat, and try to do it faster and faster. You've got rhythm!

snap clap slap snap clap slap snap clap slap

Here are some harder patterns. Again, try to do them faster and faster!

slap slap snap clap slap slap snap clap

clap slap snap clap clap slap snap clap

Here, make up a pattern of your own, using these same movements.

What are some other ways you could use the parts of your body to make a rhythm pattern? Draw and label your ideas below.

Write out your own patterns below and see how they work. Try to teach your patterns to someone else.

GAMES AND ACTIVITIES

Playing is a great way to learn new things—and of course it's a lot of fun, too! What are your favorite games to play?

Games to Play Outdoors

- marbles
- hopscotch
- softball
- hide-and-seek
- tug-of-war
- Mother, may I?
- jump rope
- jacks
- king of the hill
- leapfrog
- tag
- Simon says
- statue
- seesaw

Can you think of other games you like to play with your friends?

Things to Do by Yourself

- read
- mold clay
- play with a yo-yo
- climb on the jungle gym
- swing on the swings
- build forts
- write stories
- play with a pet
- play with toys
- do a puzzle
- play house with stuffed toys or dolls

What do you enjoy doing when you are by yourself?

Things to Learn to Do

- juggle
- swim
- throw a Frisbee™
- turn a somersault or do handstands
- paint pictures
- make and fly a kite
- grow plants

You can have your own little garden. Ask an adult where you can grow it and how to begin. Tomatoes are good plants to start with.

Remember to water your garden and weed it. A garden is a lot of work, but you will be pleased when you can pick your own tomatoes!

Another fun plant to grow is a bean plant.

You will need:

a small container
potting soil
water
dried beans

1. Fill the container with potting soil and add water to it. The soil should be damp all the way through, but not too wet. Put three dried beans into the soil and press them down about half an inch. Cover them with soil and press lightly. Place the container in a sunny window and add a little water each day.
2. In a few days you will see a sprout. Use the boxes below to draw a picture of your sprout as it looks each day for a week. Use a ruler to measure how much it grows each day.

Day 1

Height ____

Day 2

Height ____

Day 3

Height ____

Day 4

Height ____

Day 5

Height ____

Day 6

Height ____

Day 7

Height ____

Have you read *Jack and the Beanstalk*? It is a famous story about a boy who planted some magic beans. Jack grew a beanstalk that reached all the way up into the clouds. One day Jack climbed his beanstalk, and at the top he found a . . .

Draw a picture of what Jack found at the top of the beanstalk. If you don't know, or if you want to, make up your own idea. Then go to the library and check out the story!

Nature Study

A fun thing to do (by yourself or with friends) is to study life around you.

Find a corner of your backyard, a park, or a field close to your home. Try to spend a lot of time there. You can lie on the ground and be very quiet.

Make a map of everything you see. Here is what your map might look like.

You might see birds in the trees, ants coming from and going to their hill, or a beetle hurrying along. If it had rained, you might see snails in the wet ground. You'll also see many kinds of plants—grass, trees, bushes, flowers, leaves, and much more.

If you watch for an hour, you will see many things. If you come back every day to look, you will be surprised at all the different plants and animals you might see.

On a separate piece of paper, make two lists. Call one ANIMALS and the other one PLANTS. List all the different kinds of plants and animals that you might see during your nature study.

There are lots of activities that let you exercise while having fun. Here are just a few of them.

Things to Ride or Glide On

- bicycle or tricycle
- scooter
- skateboard
- wagon
- roller skates or Roller Blades

Where do you like to ride your bike? You and your friends can go riding and pretend that you are bicycling off to faraway places! You can pretend to be explorers. What places would you like to explore?

Things to Do in the Water

In the summertime, when it's warm outside, you can

- swim
- run through the hose or sprinkler
- sail toy boats
- play Marco Polo

Things to Do in the Snow

In the wintertime, when it's cold, you can do these things if it snows where you live.

- build a snow person
- make snowballs
- build a snow house
- walk on snowshoes
- slide down hills on a sled, a snow disk, a cardboard box, skis, or a bobsled

Did you know that snow is made up of millions of snowflakes that are all different?

> *If it doesn't snow where you live, there are lots of things you can do outside in winter. Can you think of anything?*
>
> *Perhaps you can do some of the things you like to do in summer. On a piece of paper, make a list of some of them.*

Not everyone is lucky enough to live in an area where winter brings snow. But you can enjoy the beauty of snow any time by making the craft below.

Colorful Snow Person

You will need:

a measuring cup
a box of laundry soap flakes
(*not* detergent)
a large bowl
water
an egg beater
scissors
blue or black construction paper
bright-colored construction paper
clear glitter

1. Pour 2 cups of soap flakes into a large bowl. Add water, a little at a time, as you mix with an egg beater.
2. When the mixture is fluffy, stop adding water. Beat with the egg beater until the mixture looks like thick whipped cream.
3. Cut out the shape of a snow person from blue or black construction paper. Use the "snow" to decorate the person. Use bits of colored paper to add details, such as eyes, ears, a nose, buttons, or a hat. The paper will stick to the soap.
4. Sprinkle clear glitter over the wet soap to make it look frosty.

Things to Do Inside

- listen to music
- dance
- sing songs

What are your favorite songs? Do you know any of these?

"Found a Peanut"
"Do Your Ears Hang Low?"
"This Old Man"
"Peanut Sat on a Railroad Track"
"Ten in the Bed"
"The Crocodile Song"
"Kookaburra"

Uh-oh! What will this peanut become if the train doesn't stop?

- do puzzles
- play cards
- play with toys
- draw pictures

> *How many objects can you draw that begin with circles?*
>
> *On a piece of paper, try to draw as much as you can, starting with circles.*
>
> *Can you draw a cat or a bicycle? Can you draw a snow person?*
>
> *There are lots more things you can draw!*

- learn tongue twisters

How fast can you repeat these silly sentences?

Rugged rubber baby buggy bumpers.

Silly Sally sells seashells by the seashore.

Slippery sleds slide smoothly.

A skunk sat on a stump. The skunk thunk the stump stunk, and the stump thunk the skunk stunk.

(Of course, there's no such word as "thunk"!)

Here are two your grandparents tried:

Peter Piper picked a peck of pickled peppers.

How much wood would a woodchuck chuck if a woodchuck could chuck wood?

If you can say those tongue twisters, try this longer one:

Moses supposes his toeses
are roses.
This poses a puzzle, you see.
For nobody's toeses are
posies of roses
As Moses supposes his
toeses to be.

Make up a tongue twister of your own. The picture in the box will get you started! Use the Word Bank if you need help.

Word Bank:

penguins	perky	pink	petunia
pizza	pretty	party	pal
purple	pop	penny	popcorn

Wordoodles

Here is a fun way to play with words. You can write words in a way that helps to explain what they mean. Look at these examples.

Now try to draw some wordoodles of your own, using the words below.

falling **smile**

short **explode**

Use another piece of paper to make up lots more wordoodles!

- read books

Have you read any of these books?

The Little Engine That Could
Pippi Longstocking
The Wind in the Willows
Hansel and Gretel
Curious George
Heidi
Cinderella

What is your favorite story? Why do you like it? What happens in the story?

There are some animal stories listed on page 48. Would you rather read about animals or people?

What story could you tell to go with this picture?

Have you ever acted out a story you know well?
Have you ever acted out a story you made up?
The next time you have friends over, see if you can act out a story. You can ask other friends or your family to watch.

- make your own book

Here's how. First you think up a story.

How does the story begin? What happens? How does the story end?

Then you take several sheets of paper and fold them in half, like this:

Think of a name for your book. Write this name on the outside piece of paper. If you cannot do this yourself, ask someone to help you.

On the inside pages, write your story. If you need help, you can ask someone to write the words. But make sure the words are your own. Draw pictures on each page so people can see what is happening in the story.

When you have come to the end of your story, you have written a book!

Can you finish this story?

Story Starters

What do you think is happening in this picture? Fill in the lines below to tell what each character is thinking or feeling.

Man: ____

____

____

____

Dog: ____

____

____

____

Crocodile: ____

____

____

____

Here, write a story about the picture on page 70. Before you begin, think about your story. Make sure it has a beginning, a middle, and an end. Use another piece of paper if you need more room to write.

Does your story have a happy ending? Circle each character that is happy at the end of your story.

- watch movies

Have you seen any of these movies?

Charlie and the Chocolate Factory
The Wizard of Oz
The Little Mermaid
Aladdin
Snow White and the Seven Dwarfs
Alice in Wonderland
Beauty and the Beast
Peter Pan
Hook
Popeye
Pinocchio
101 Dalmatians

- watch television

What is your favorite TV program? Do you watch any of these shows?

Sesame Street
Barney & Friends
Mister Rogers' Neighborhood
Toon Town Kids
Reading Rainbow
Lamb Chop's Play-Along
The Biker Mice From Mars
The Adventures of Sonic the Hedgehog

Movies are made by using a special camera. This camera can take a series of pictures very quickly on a long strip of film. When the film is shown on a screen, the pictures (about 24 each second!) appear to move.

You can make a moving-picture book! Think of a simple event you would like to show. For example: a balloon rising through the air, a frog jumping from the shore into a pond, or a tree falling.

You will need:

3" tall by 5" wide white, unlined cards, cut in half
a pencil or marker
a stapler

1. On the cards, draw a series of at least 10 pictures that show the event from beginning to end. Put only one picture on each card. Make sure to draw the pictures the same size. Place each one near the right-hand side of the card.
2. When you are done, staple the pages in order. Put the staples down the left-hand side of the book.
3. Hold the book in your left hand and, using your right thumb, quickly flip the pages. To do this, slide your thumb over the edges of your book, from the top of the stack to the bottom.

- make yummy foods to eat

Everybody needs to eat, so everybody should know how to fix food.

Here are some good things you can fix for yourself and your friends, any time of year. You can ask your mom or dad for help if you need it.

Before you start to make the food, wash your hands. Then make sure you have everything you need.

Peanut Butter and Banana Sandwich

For each sandwich, you will need:

2 slices of bread
a banana
peanut butter
a plate
a table knife (*not* a sharp knife)

1. Put both slices of bread on the plate. Spread some peanut butter on each slice, using the knife.
2. Wash the knife, then cut the banana into little rounds.
3. Lay the rounds close together on one piece of bread. (You may have more banana rounds than can fit on the bread. What can you do with the extras?)
4. Put the other slice of bread on top of the banana rounds.

You have made a sandwich!

Date-Nut Cream Cheese Sandwich

For each sandwich, you will need:

2 slices of bread
cream cheese
dates, with the pits already taken out
(enough to cover a slice of bread)
walnuts, already out of their shells
(enough to cover a slice of bread)
a plate
a table knife (*not* a sharp knife)

1. Put both slices of bread on the plate. Use the knife to spread some cream cheese on each slice.
2. Open the dates and put them close together on top of the cream cheese.
3. Put the walnuts between the dates.
4. Place the second slice of bread on top of the first slice, then munch on your sandwich!

More than two hundred years ago a man named the Earl of Sandwich was busy playing a game. He was hungry, but he did not want to stop. He told someone, "Bring me two slices of bread with some meat in between." This was the first sandwich, and so "sandwiches" were named for him!

You can put all sorts of food between two slices of bread to make a sandwich. Why don't you make up some sandwiches of your own? You can try them out on your family and friends.

Everybody likes cold lemonade in the hot summer. But you can drink it all year long. Here is how you make enough for two glasses.

Lemonade

You will need:

1 lemon, cut in half (ask a grown-up to help)
2 tablespoons of sugar
ice cubes
water
a lemon squeezer
a small bowl
a tablespoon
a glass

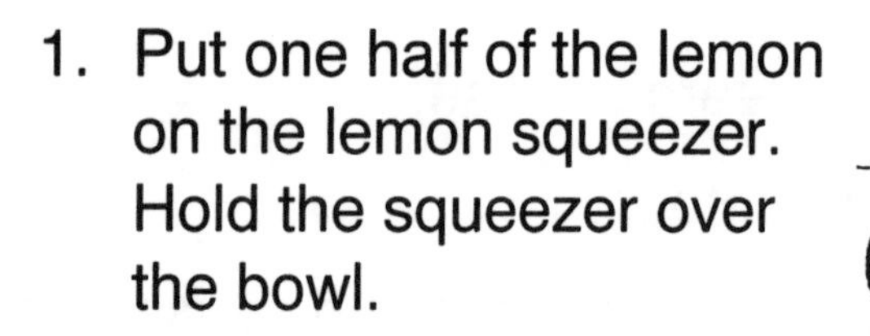

1. Put one half of the lemon on the lemon squeezer. Hold the squeezer over the bowl.

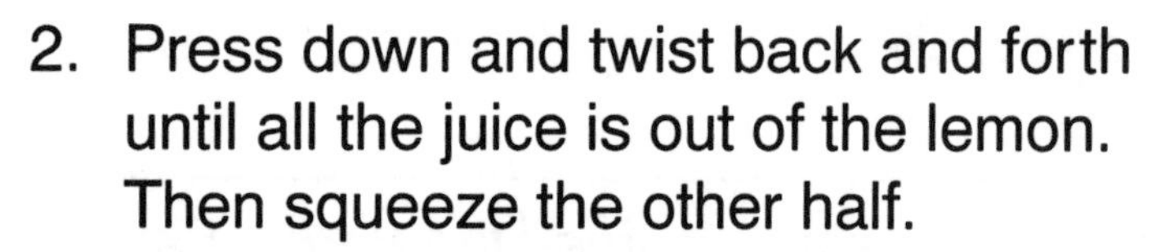

2. Press down and twist back and forth until all the juice is out of the lemon. Then squeeze the other half.

3. Dip the tablespoon into the sugar and get a spoonful. Pour the sugar into the lemon juice without touching the juice. Then dip the spoon into the sugar and get another spoonful. Put the sugar into the juice.
4. Stir the sugar into the lemon juice with the spoon, until all the sugar is gone.

5. Put ice cubes in the glass, then pour in half the lemon juice mixture.
6. Add water to fill the glass, then stir.
7. Taste the lemonade. If it is not sweet enough, you can add a little sugar.

You will have enough lemonade left over to have another glass. You can save it in the refrigerator. Or, you can share the lemonade with a friend!

Most people drink lemonade in the afternoon. You can even have it at lunchtime, with a sandwich you have made!

Here are two food jokes. Do you know any others?

What do you call a cat that likes lemonade?

A sour puss.

What two things can you never have for lunch?

Breakfast and dinner.

Silly Soup

The cooks at Rhonda's Wretched Restaurant need a recipe for Silly Soup. Can you help? Below, list the ingredients you would need to make Silly Soup.

2 quarts ______________________________

1 pint ________________________________

1 cup _________________________________

3 ________________________, finely chopped

1 tablespoon __________________________

½ teaspoon ___________________________

____

____

Here, write down how you would make Silly Soup.

____

____

____

____

____

____

Here is a wonderful game you can play. It doesn't need any equipment, and you can play it anywhere—in the car, by a campfire, or at the dinner table. The game can be about anything in the world!

20 Questions

1. The player who is "it" must think of any object. He or she then tells the other players if this object is "animal," "vegetable," or "mineral."
    - **Animal** would be any person or animal, or anything made from animal products, such as meat or leather shoes.
    - **Vegetable** would be any plant or tree, or anything made from plants or trees, such as paper, wooden furniture, or cotton clothing.
    - **Mineral** would be anything made of inorganic (non-plant and non-animal) materials, such as metal or glass.
2. The players then ask the person who is "it" 20 questions about the object. Each question must be answered "yes" or "no." For example, a player may ask, "Is it bigger than a basketball?" but not "How big is it?"
3. The players try to guess the object from what they have learned. If a player guesses correctly, it is his or her turn to be "it." If no one can guess after 20 questions, the person who is "it" must tell the answer.

AN ALMANAC IS . . .

As you can see, an almanac is a book about almost everything. It is a great place to look for information or ideas, but it's not the only place! If there is something you want to know more about, look it up in an encyclopedia. Make sure you always have a dictionary close by. And an atlas will come in handy if you are trying to find out more about places in the world.

The library is an information treasure chest. Ask an adult to show you how to use the card catalog to look up books on any subject. You will find lots of books in your library that will help you.

Below, make a list of subjects or ideas that interest you. Use your atlas, almanac, dictionary, encyclopedia, and library to find out all about them!